DOWN,

In The Valley

Arthur De Anda

Arthur De Anda

Dedication

In the loving memory of Ruben Flores.

About the Author

Art's Life Story

Arthur De Anda is a self-taught writer, A Father & A Grandfather.

Who grew up in a small San Gabriel Valley neighborhood.

He worked for 32 long years as a union carpenter all over Southern California.

He is now retired and wants to share with the world some of his stories and talk about many of the lessons that he has learned over the years of his life.

Arthur De Anda

My name is Rene Ayala. My story began a long time ago when I was a small boy growing up in the San Fernando Valley (Pacoima), Ca. I lived with my mother and father, Emilia and Ernesto Ayala, who I thought got along great, but it turned out they never really got along at all. They argued and fought a lot which led to their separation when I was a young boy. My mother moved back into her mom's house, Grandma Rose, down in San Fernando, and my father moved back to a ranch in Texas owned by his family. The ranch had horses, cows, goats, and many other animals. As a young boy growing up in the early 1980s, it was tough for my mom to raise me all by herself.

This made her have to work really hard to take care of me, so I always wanted to make her proud by trying to do good in school and trying to stay out of trouble. But somehow, trouble always had its way of finding me; fighting at school, shoplifting, etc. I recall a time when one of my friends lit a whole field on fire. I wasn't there, but in Mom's eyes, I was, and she would have her own little way of punishing me by shipping me off to Texas and making me spend summers with my father on the ranch.

My father was raised in Mexico on a ranch just like the one in Texas by his father and grandfather. My father was strict, but he was very good to me and showed me a lot of love, so I didn't mind spending my summers in Texas. I would work on the ranch feeding the animals, cleaning the horse stables, chasing the chickens around, and learning a lot about what it was like to live on a ranch. Funny enough, whenever we ate, it was almost always something that was grown or raised on the ranch.

However, I wasn't always working. I got to ride horses, shoot guns, and listen to my father tell stories about my grandfather and his own childhood growing up on a ranch. He would always remind me of the importance of raising a family of your own and how it was the key to becoming a man. I remember my father had an ATC three-wheeler for dragging the dirt in the arena and weeds all around the land, which somehow became part of my weekly chores.

He would get mad at me because I would always disappear on the ATC, riding it all around the trails that surrounded the land. I had so much fun on the ranch that I didn't want to go back home at the end of summer. But summer would end, and I would be driven back home by my father and one of his ranch hands, Mingo. He would always come inside, talk to my mom, say his goodbyes, give me a big hug, and a hand full of money for helping him on the ranch. It wasn't a lot, but good enough to buy some cool-looking school clothes and still have some cash left over.

I started hanging out with one of the local street gangs and ended up in trouble every now and then. I began getting into fights, some stealing, and graffiti. More so, I even started drinking and smoking marijuana. My mom would always threaten me, saying, "I am going to ship you off to the ranch permanently!" And it always used to end with a one-hour phone call with my dad, who would remind me all about life, my future, and becoming a man.

As I grew older, I met a girl in my junior year in high school, Isabell Garcia. She was so damn beautiful, and I think I fell in love the first time I laid my eyes on her. I started spending most of my time with her and not much with my friends, with whom I got in all the trouble. Her parents, Adrian and Elena Garcia, raised her right. She belonged to a decent family and was not at all involved in any of the street crap like me. Isabell and I got really close in that school year and were both falling in love, so much so that I did not go to the ranch that summer. I spent every minute that I could with her.

My senior year in high school was very hard, and her love made me work extra so that we could graduate together and make everyone proud of me – Mom, Dad, Isabell, and her Parents. Her parents appreciated that I worked extra hard to graduate from high school with her. I was head over heels in love with her. We graduated high school and started our future together. I went to trade school to become an electrician, and she started working for the city of Pacoima school district.

Finally, we got married and began our beautiful lives together. I was a Union Electrician working downtown LA and all-over southern California while she still worked for the school district. Life was good. On a sad note, my Grandma Rose had passed, and my mother inherited her home in San Fernando, where she wanted us to live so that she would not be all alone.

Down, In The Valley

So, my wife and I moved in with her right in my old neighborhood. Life was good, and we were doing well. Thus, we decided to start a family.

Soon enough, we had two boys one year apart, Rene Jr and Robert. They were the greatest thing in the world to us. They went to all the same schools we went to as kids, and we tried our best to bring them upright in a troubled neighborhood. I always reminded them of all the trouble I got into as a kid growing up there with the gangs and how hard it was to get out of all that and turn my life around after being involved in drinking and drugs and hoping that they would not follow in my footsteps.

My wife and I had another boy after five years of our last child, Rudy – our youngest son. So now, we had three boys growing up in that damn neighborhood. Ultimately, the great life we were living started to become problematic for all of us. Nonetheless, I always told my boys my childhood stories about how I used to get in trouble, how their Grandma Lita would ship me off to Grandpa's ranch, and everything I could to keep them on the straight path throughout their lives. But it all backfired on us.

Years went by, and we, as parents, did all the sports with our children and the fun activities, including going to Disneyland, Knots Berry Farm, and camping. The boys were now in high school, and my wife and I got so busy with work and life that time just seemed to zip by. Part of the reason was Grandma Lita got diagnosed with breast cancer and became very sick. So, my wife and I spent all our spare time at hospitals and doctor's appointments, making us lose track of what was going on with our boys. They started dressing like little gangsters, hanging out with the local neighborhood boys. Phone calls from school started coming in about them getting into trouble here and there, which made us even have to go down to the police station to pick them up for crimes like stealing a bike, smoking weed, fighting at school, etc. We just lost track of everything that was going on around us.

Grandma Lita ended up losing her battle with Breast Cancer, which just broke all of our hearts. We took time off from work and school and just moped around the house for a while. One day, when I was on the phone with my father, telling him all my sad stories, he came up with a great idea, suggesting that we get away from the city and go to the ranch in Texas for a couple of weeks. I discussed it with my wife, and we both thought it would be a great idea to get the boys up there; maybe it would be the turnaround we had been looking for.

Not only would it get them away for a while, but they would finally be able to spend some time with their grandfather. Meanwhile, I thought, *yes, like me get them up there, and they would do all the things I did when I was a kid.* The two older boys suggested staying behind and remaining home, but my wife and I were not having it. So, we all packed up, and off we went to Texas to Grandpa Ernie's ranch.

Down, In The Valley

My dad knew about the trouble we had been having with the boys in good old San Fernando Valley, so by the time we got there, he was ready for us. He had daily chores all lined up, from cleaning the horse corrals, dragging all the dirt with the same old ATC that I used to do it with, to feeding the animals, which they had no idea was probably going to be dinner.

At first, they complained and said, "Dad! We are not doing any of this crap."

But they joined in when they saw their 60-year-old grandpa and all of his ranch hands up at the crack of dawn doing all the chores that the ranch had to offer.

Even my wife and I joined in and helped out. Just like with me, it didn't always work. Grandpa would take the boys out for some fun every day; they learned to ride the horses, went out shooting, fishing down at the lake, and jammed out on the ATC every now and then. They all started to have a lot of fun and forget all about the crap back home.

Two weeks went by, and now, it was time for us to get back to good old San Fernando Valley and our old lives back home. As we were getting packed up to leave, all three boys came up to me and their mom and asked, "Mom! Dad! Can we stay longer?" We could not be happier, so we both called our jobs back home and decided to stay for another week. The week went by so fast, and the boys had so much fun, enjoying their time with their grandpa. You know, I hadn't seen my father in years, but I noticed a different kind of happiness in him this time that I had never seen before. He truly enjoyed spending time with his grandsons.

After a week, we all came back home and fell right back into our old routines. My wife and I went back to work and the kids to school. Our youngest son, Rudy, was now in high school, Robert was finishing high school, and Junior was working at a local body shop that had been around for years. He liked Lowrider cars and wanted to paint and restore them one day. He seemed to be doing fine, getting up every day, going to work, and even helping his mom with paying bills. He also bought himself a used car and seemed to be doing pretty well, or so we thought.

One night, we were relaxing at home when the phone started ringing. It turned out our son was in jail for some grand theft auto charge. He claimed it was not him, but he ended up taking a plea and getting six months in jail. My wife and I were devastated. Robert was out of school and was working for a local construction company doing room additions and different construction locally.

Our youngest boy, Rudy, was in high school, and my wife and I watched him closely since we did not want him to follow in his brother's footsteps; not that my eldest son was all bad, but we just didn't want him getting in any trouble. I thought that they needed girlfriends because that's what worked for me.

Down, In The Valley

Four months went by, and Junior came back home. He started working back at the body shop, trying to stay out of trouble as he was now on probation. Robert was still working in construction, and Rudy was still in high school. All in all, life seemed to be on track once again, and my wife and I were very happy. The boys were staying out of trouble, and our youngest was doing great in high school. Also, my wife and I were both doing well in our careers. Other than the boys not having steady girlfriends and a few gang-looking tattoos, life was good.

Time was flying by, and I hadn't talked to my father for a while. One Saturday afternoon, the phone rang, and it was Pop's, calling to see how we all were doing. We started talking, and I tried to explain why I hadn't called him in so long. The next thing he said shook me.

"I am visiting to look at some property. I am planning to sell the ranch and move out to be closer to the boys and you," he stated. "I am looking at 20 acres just outside of Apple Valley, Ca. in a small town called Lucerne Valley."

The news made us all very excited that my father was moving to California, and we would be able to visit and see him regularly. After a few months, my father made his big move from Texas to Lucerne Valley with a bit of help from some of his Texas friends in bringing a couple of big trailers, four horses, and some of the animals - his Dogs and one of his best ranch hand buddies, Domingo aka Mingo – to CA. I talked to my dad, and he told me that they were getting settled in.

“When are you planning to come up and visit?” He asked.

“We will be up one of these weekends. We can’t wait to see you!” I told him. He then gave me all the directions to his place, and we made plans to visit him the following weekend.

On Saturday, my wife, our youngest son, and I headed out to a town called Lucerne Valley in the High Desert, about 80 miles from San Fernando Valley. We came up through a small town in the middle of nowhere. When I say small, I mean small, like no markets, one or two gas stations, and no fast-food restaurants anywhere; the little guy, as I called my youngest son, didn’t like it at all. It was an open desert as far as the eye could see. We made a left turn on the street called Hwy 247 and went right through the middle of the desert, about halfway to I-40, the Hwy to Arizona.

Along the mountains on the left, we saw some trailers, trucks, dust, and the sign my dad told us to look for when we got about 12 miles up. We made a left turn up the tiny dirt road and saw my father and Mingo working on the ranch, which I later nicknamed the Ponderosa. He had done so much; he had got two big trailers, a huge storage container, sheds, horse corrals, and a big ass arena just like the one in Texas. I saw a huge water tank that looked just like the one in the Texas Ranch.

Down, In The Valley

We pulled up, and Dad seemed very happy to see us. He immediately asked where the older boys were, and we told him that they had to work. I could not believe all the work that had been done in such a short time. As I was snooping around, I noticed a Mini Kawasaki Truck sticking out of the storage container. Dad said he bought that for doing work around the land and that he could drive it all through the desert. I was getting a closer look when I noticed he had brought the old ATC with him that I used to ride in Texas. I asked him if it still worked, and he said, "That thing takes a licken', but keeps on ticken,'" in his Texas Accent, which made me laugh.

He and Mingo took us all for a ride through the desert in the Kawasaki Mule, which we later nicknamed 'The little Mule.' It had a front and back bench seat, which could ride up to six people, and a small truck bed. He took us through the trails all along the mountains and dirt roads everywhere. Every now and then, we came up on someone's private property. There were tiny houses in the middle of nowhere and an open desert everywhere we looked.

My father kept saying how he really liked that part of being out there. He even took us to a small fenced-in area that they called 'The plane crash.' It looked like some kind of gravesite to me. All in all, we spent about half the day up there and promised Dad and Mingo that we would come up and spend a weekend with all the boys. We got home and told the boys all about our day at the Ponderosa, trying our best to make it sound like a lot of fun so that they would want to go up and spend time out there and visit Pops and Mingo. We mainly wanted them to do something other than hanging out in the good old San Fernando Valley.

So, a couple of weeks went by, and my wife and I were trying to figure out ways of getting the boys wanting to visit the Ponderosa. At the same time, we were wondering how we would be able to spend the weekend up there. It was such a far journey to get there and really not worth it to go just for a day. Dad had mentioned that we could sleep in one of the trailers, but we didn't want him or Mingo to change their sleeping arrangements.

So later that week, when I was driving home from work, I noticed that one of my neighbors was selling an old Motor Home. I got home and told my wife about the RV down the street. We both agreed that this was a great idea. We waited for the weekend and went down to talk to the neighbors about their Motor Home. It was an older one but hardly ever used. It was a mid-90s model, had low miles on it, and was very nice inside.

They were asking $15,000 for it, which was a lot of money, so we made them an offer of $12,000. They took it. We were very excited and could not wait to pack up the New RV and go out camping at the Ponderosa. The boys were excited about the new big house on wheels that was parked in the driveway but not as excited as the little one. He could not wait to go back and spend the weekend up there.

So, we called Dad and told him the good news about 'Big Bertha,' our RV. He was just as excited as we were, so we made plans to visit him the following weekend. Of course, our two elder shits made excuses on why they could not go, so my wife, the little guy, and I took off for the weekend to have fun visiting Dad and Mingo at the Ponderosa. We set out on Friday right after we got home from work; Big Bertha was all packed up and ready to go. Even though there was traffic throughout the way, something about driving in the RV was just so comfortable that we didn't even notice the traffic.

We finally got there, and Dad and Mingo were outside waiting for us. They had a cool spot all set up for us to park. It took me a while to get all set up, as it was my first time with Big Bertha. By the time I was all set up, it was already dark. To tell the truth, it was very spooky out at the Ponderosa at night as there was no power. Dad had it all set up with a big generator to run power for the two trailers, plus Big Bertha had a generator of her own. Dad had placed small solar-powered lights all around the campsite so that it looked like someone was there at night.

It was quiet, peaceful, and beautiful out there at night. I looked up, and there were like a billion stars in the sky with no police sirens, helicopters, cars crashing, or any of the big city noises that we were used to hearing. Dad and Mingo had chairs set up around a cool fire pit that they had dug into the ground. Mingo was firing it up.

We were not used to living like this, but you have to take my word for it, it was amazing out there! Sitting around the campfire, Dad and Mingo told different stories about the time we were all at the ranch in Texas. It started to get late, and my wife fell asleep in her chair. So, we all got ready for bed, and Dad took the little guy to walk the land and lock up the front gate. It was time for us all to crash for the night.

The sun rose and woke me up at around 5 A.M. I peeked out of the RV window and saw Dad and Mingo already awake, busy in their morning chores out by the horse stables. They were feeding the horses, cleaning the stables, and making sure they had fresh water, which reminded me of my summers at the ranch in Texas. Dad had a whole day all planned out for him, Mingo, and the little guy; horseback riding, shooting, and taking off in the little mule. My wife and I stayed back and enjoyed the time off from work and being away from the big city. As we were sitting outside, my wife and I started to figure out ways to get the two little shits back home to come out and have some fun at the Ponderosa.

As we were sitting there, a small pack of riders on dirt bikes and ATVs went by us. We waved at them, and they all waved back. Right that very moment, the light bulb in my head went off, and I said to my wife, "Hey, wouldn't it be a great idea if we got a couple of those for the boys? I bet it would get them to come and hang out with us instead of being back home."

She agreed with me. So, after a nice but short weekend of relaxation and fun, we headed back to the big city. We didn't tell the little guy about our big plan. During the week, we googled and found a bunch of stores that sold

ATVs. One of the guys at work told me about a big store in the city of Covina that sold ATVs called Bert's Mega Mall. I made some phone calls and set up an appointment for the following Saturday morning. We went down to this Mega Mall, met the sales guy Jacob, and we started wheeling and dealing without realizing how expensive it was going to be. Just one ATV costs up to $10,000, which made my wife and me discuss all of the ins and outs of making a major purchase like this, deciding that family and future are one of the most important things in life and you only get to live it once.

Somehow, Jacob talked us into buying not one, but three bikes - two ATVs and one 2-wheeled Dirt Bike. We went all out and bought helmets, boots, gloves, and goggles as well. We even had to buy two big-ass gear bags to keep it all in. Just when we were about done, the sales guy asked us how we were planning to get all this stuff home. I had my truck with me, but there was no way everything was going to fit in the back. So, we then realized that we also needed to buy a trailer to haul all the bikes home. Trust me, we must have financed around $30,000 that day.

All done at Bert's Megamall, we headed back home with a huge trailer full of brand-new toys all hooked up to the back of my Truck with my wife and me wondering if this was a good idea. As we were pulling up back home, I started honking the horn. All three boys just so happened to be home, and none of them was more excited than the little guy as he already knew how nice it was up at the Ponderosa and that he could finally have some fun with his two older brothers. After we got Big Bertha out of the way and put all the new toys in the garage, we began making the big plans of getting the whole tribe up to the Ponderosa for some well-needed family fun.

Finally, we had a nice weekend coming up where we were all free, and it just so happened to be a three-day weekend of Memorial Day. I made everyone take Friday off so that we could get an early start on the big fun. We got all packed up on Thursday Night to get on the road early Friday morning with the Dirt Bike trailer all hooked up to the back of Big Bertha. My wife, the little one, and I were in the RV, and the two elder rascals were following behind in the older one's car as they didn't want to ride in Big Bertha. They wanted to drive themselves in case they decided to leave early. It was a very nice drive up to Lucerne Valley; there was no traffic, and it was smooth sailing all the way there.

Just as we were about to make the left turn onto HWY 247, I realized that we needed to fill up all the gas cans for the Dirt Bikes. So, I pulled up to a gas station on the right-hand side just before the left turn at HWY 247, with the two boys following close behind. I got out of the RV and told the boys to get all of the gas cans ready so that we could fill them up. As the little one and I headed into the store, I noticed two white dudes hanging out in front of the store, both with jailhouse tattoos and around my two elder boys' ages.

Down, In The Valley

As I was in the store, the two young men approached the dirt bike trailer and began telling my boys how nice the bikes were and asked them where we were headed. Robert, my second youngest, looked up and noticed that one of them had a humongous tattoo across his back that read, 'Lucerne Valley' with the 'Valley' written very big underneath the Lucerne. He told his brother, who had a similar tattoo on his back that read 'San Fernando Valley' with the 'Valley' very large as well.

The two little shits started to talk crap at the two white dudes, commenting about their tattoos. I came out of the store and butted in, yelling at my boys to start filling up the gas cans. I went over to help them and gave them a bunch of shit about starting trouble at the store and reminded them that we were not out there for that kind of crap. At last, we pulled out, making the left turn onto HWY 247, all excited about the big fun weekend out at the Ponderosa.

As we pulled up to the land, Dad and Mingo were awaiting our arrival. Dad helped in directing me to the same parking spot that I was in before. We parked Big Bertha and started unloading all our stuff. The boys helped out, as we were all very excited. As we got Big Bertha set up, the boys got all the Dirt Bikes unloaded. Dad and Mingo both walked up and hugged the boys. I could tell Dad was very happy that all of his boys were up for a visit. Grandpa started to tell them about all the stuff he had planned out for them, but I could tell that the boys couldn't wait to ride the new 'Toys.' We shot the shit with Gramps and Mingo for a while, but the boys could not wait to go for a ride.

As the boys got all geared up, their mom gave them a bunch of crap about not taking off too far, getting hurt, lost, and keeping a close eye on their little brother. They could ride somewhat from riding the ATC back in Texas. The little one, Rudy, had already been out there, so he was telling his brothers about the different areas that he had seen when he was out there that time with grandpa and Mingo on the mule. He had seen some riders out there, riding at a cool track location, and told the boys that he was going to take them out there. So now they were finally all geared up. They took off on all three bikes with their mom shouting out for them to be careful.

My wife was a little worried but tried not to show it. She looked over and asked me, “Do you think they are going to be okay?”

“Hey, stop worrying about them. It is not like back home, where we have to worry about them every time they walk out the door,” I replied.

She agreed, and so we started to enjoy the peacefulness of being out at the Ponderosa. As we were sitting back, relaxing, and enjoying our time, we heard some bikes coming from the back side of the land. We thought it was the boys, but it was three guys on Dirt Bikes heading in the same direction that the boys took off. We didn’t think anything of it as the riders waved as they passed by.

Down, In The Valley

The little one, Rudy, had taken the boys to check out the track that he had seen when he was out there with Grandpa. As the boys were racing each other around the track, the three riders that rode past us came into the track area and started jumping and riding their bikes crazily near the boys, zipping by real fast and shooting dirt and rocks up at the boys with their back tires as if the boys were invading their turf. The boys did not think anything of it as they were not as experienced as the three boys. They just continued to ride all around the desert, with Rudy showing them the different spots their grandpa had shown him. He even took them to the plane crash area that Grandpa took us all to when we went out in the little mule.

Finally, they made it back to the land where I was getting ready to Barbeque Cheese Burgers for lunch. As they were hanging out at the RV, they didn't stop talking all about the ride they had just got back from. My wife and I smiled and kissed as we were extremely happy to see the boys having so much fun.

That night, we all sat around the campfire. Mom got the idea to roast marshmallows in the fire from the last time we were out there. As the boys were eating the marshmallows, they could not stop talking about the ride they had gone on that day. Again, my wife and I just smiled and felt so satisfied with our decision to buy those toys. *Oh, what a great idea it was getting the boys away from the big city life,* I thought to myself.

The next morning, Dad had the day all planned out for him, Mingo, and the boys to have some ranch fun; horseback riding, training the horses in the big arena, and going out shooting guns. My wife and I watched as the boys tried to ride the horses. It was so funny as you could tell they were afraid of them. They rode a bit in Texas but not enough to be cowboys.

Then, we all went back into the mountains to shoot Dad's guns. My wife stayed back as she wanted to make lunch for all of us. Dad had a few guns, mostly rifles, shotguns, and a couple of handguns. We had never really shotguns or skeet before. Dad had a skeet launcher mounted to the hitch of the little mule where it would throw the skeet up in the air, and you would shoot it with a shotgun before it hit the ground.

Boy, it was fun! Myself, Dad, Mingo, and Rudy headed back to the Ponderosa in the little mule. The boys had taken the 2 ATVs out there, so they said that they would come back in a bit. I did not think anything of it.

Back at the RV, my wife and I were sitting outside when we heard gunshots back in the mountains where the boys were. So, I jumped up and got into the little mule, and headed back out there. I noticed that the boys were already heading back, so I asked them about the gunshots, and they started acting all stupid. It turned out that the two little shits had brought a handgun from back home and decided to shoot it up at the land.

I got so mad at them both and started giving them all kinds of shit about the gun. I made them give me the gun and told them a million reasons why they shouldn't have a gun. My middle son, Robert, told me that the gun was his and that he had bought it through legal means back home from one of the local Pawn Shops. I was very mad at them and said, "I will give it back to you when we get home, but I do not want you guys having guns while you live in our house!"

After a while, I calmed down as I did not want to ruin the fun that we were having out at the land. When we got back to the land, I snuck the gun into Dad's storage container and hid it way in the back corner. I did not want my wife to know, so I told her that the gunshots must have been from somewhere else. The weekend continued, and the boys rode the bikes non-stop. They seemed to be having so much fun, with the little one having the most as he would constantly tell his brothers, "Let's go out for a ride." We could not get him off the Bikes; he was having the time of his life!

Monday morning came around, and we had Big Bertha all loaded up for the long ride back home. The only thing left was to load up all the bikes. As we were getting ready to load the bikes up, Dad asked me how I felt towing all the bikes and trailer behind the RV.

"It kind of sucks. I am barely getting used to the Motor Home, let alone hauling a trailer behind it," I ranted. "Moreover, it is a bitch back home making room for all the new toys."

Hearing my bluster, he suggested that we lock all the stuff up in his storage container and park the trailer in the back corner. So that way, all we had to do was load up Big Bertha and head out. My wife and I thought it was a great idea, so we went ahead and put all the bikes in the container along with all the gear and parked the trailer in the back. This was going to save us a lot of work back home. Driving back home with Rudy, talking non-stop about all the fun he had out there and how he could not wait to go back, my wife and I just looked at each other and just smiled. We were so happy that the boys had so much fun and that they spent time with their grandfather.

Finally, back home, while I was unloading Big Bertha, Robert, our middle son, got me alone and asked me if he could have his gun back. Right away, I thought to myself, *Oh Shit, I left it hiding in the storage container!* I told him, and he was mad.

"As soon as I got a chance, I would go up and get it for you. But I still do not want that thing in my house," He agreed and promised he would get rid of it as soon as he got it back. It was kind of hard for me to go back up right away as my wife did not know about the gun. So, I waited for a good reason to go back up, not knowing that a hellified reason was coming my way.

After about two weeks, at around 1:30 in the morning, we heard a banging at the front door. I answered the door only to find out that it was the San Fernando Police Department. They asked for me and then inquired if I owned an ATV motorcycle. They gave me the plate number, to which I replied in affirmation. It turned out the Lucerne Valley Sherriff Station had called them and told them that they found it in the desert. He gave them my name and address and asked if they could notify me that my bike had been stolen. I took a sigh of relief that I was not wanted for some unknown warrant or crime. I asked for the phone number of the Lucerne Sheriff Station, and like a bolt of lightning, I said, "Oh shit, GRANDPA!"

I called the Sheriff's Station as fast as I could and told them who I was and all about the ATV they found and where it was stolen from. I explained to them, saying, "My father lives out at the land where it was stolen from. You need to get out there ASAP to check on my dad!" So, I gave them the directions to the land and requested them to hurry since I feared that something might be wrong because Dad would have called me if there was a break-in.

So, Mom and I got dressed as fast as we could, woke up the boys, and told them what was going on. We hauled our asses as fast as we could to the land, with my wife telling me to slow down all the way there since I was driving like a maniac. Finally, we made the left turn on HWY 247. It was pitch black out as there were no street lights, and in the far distance, we could see all the lights of the Police vehicles, Fire Trucks, Ambulances, and Rescue Squads.

We drove up the dirt road swiftly and saw an ambulance with someone inside. I jumped out of my car and ran towards the front gate, only to be stopped by a Sheriff named Manuel Gonzales. I told him who I was and that my father lived there with his good friend Mingo. He told me that my father was fine and that he was getting checked out by the paramedics. Sheriff Gonzales let us go in to see my father, but on the way, another officer named Kevin Sorbal stopped us.

He was trying to get a statement from Dad about what had happened. He was a real ass hole with my wife and me as we tried to get to Dad to make sure he was okay. Sheriff Gonzales must have heard all the commotion going on and came over to us. He got in between us and started to calm everyone down. He took Sheriff Sorbal to the side, and soon after, they let us go up to the ambulance where my dad was being kept.

He was very shaken up and would not stop going on about Mingo. It turned out that before we got there, Mingo had been taken to the hospital with a very serious head injury. Dad had been roughed up pretty well too, but he seemed good. I finally got Dad to calm down and tell us what had happened. As he was telling us what happened, the sheriffs were writing it all down.

"The dog was barking, but I did not think anything of it because he always barks. I then heard some strange noises out by the storage container and people talking. So I got my shotgun and thought that I had better go and check it out," Dad stated. "As I began to step out of my trailer, I was hit from behind, causing me to fall to the floor. I looked up and noticed that they had already taken Mingo out of the other trailer, and he was on the ground, also."

Down, In The Valley

"How many men were there?" The sheriff asked Dad.

"There were around four or five of them," he replied. "They were asking for money and items that may be worth any money. The only money that we had on the land was what was in our wallets. I told them that we had no money and to please leave us alone. But they started ram-sacking the trailers, looking for cash and valuables. I again begged them to please leave Mingo and me alone. Then, one of the guys asked what was inside the storage container, and I told them there was just feed and hay for the horses. They asked me to open up the container. I tried to lie and said I could not find the key, but they started to rough up Mingo to get me to open up the storage container. As they were hitting Mingo, he swung back at one of them, hitting him in the face. The guy picked up a steel post and hit Mingo in the head, knocking him unconscious. As the guy went to strike Mingo again, I yelled for him to stop and that I would open up the container."

"I then opened up the storage container, and the guys went in," Dad continued to narrate. "I could hear them cheering and saying how they hit the Jackpot. As all of the dust cleared, they left Mingo and me lying there on the ground. They ram-sacked both trailers and took all three new bikes, all of the gear that we had purchased, and all of Dad's guns. They didn't take the little mule as they could not get it started. They loaded what they could in their truck, but two of them actually rode the ATVs right out the gate."

As the paramedics and fire trucks were leaving, Dad mentioned that he wanted to go to the hospital to check on Mingo. As both officer Gonzales and Sorbal were still there wrapping up their investigation, Sheriff Sorbal reminded me that he had my ATV, and it was still back at the sheriff's station.

"You will have to come in and file a report on the other bikes and your dad's guns," the sheriff told me.

Of course, none of Dad's guns were ever registered as they were old guns from Mexico and Texas. So, my wife jumped in her truck and took Dad to the hospital to check on Mingo, and I went to the sheriff's station in Dad's Truck to file a report and pick up the one ATV that was confiscated in the middle of the desert. As I was driving to the station, I noticed that Sheriff Sorbal was driving behind me all the way there. I got to the station at the same time Sheriff Sorbal pulled up.

We walked in together, and I swear this station reminded me of an old small-town Police Station from the 1950s. We went inside, where Sheriff Sorbal was the only one there. He started asking me for all the information about the bikes and the paperwork for Dad's guns. But at the end of the day, I had none of the above.

Consequently, I told the sheriff that I did not have the paperwork for the bikes as it was all at home. "Also, I do not think that any of Dad's guns were registered, as they were bought a long time ago," I said.

Down, In The Valley

The sheriff started acting like an ass, saying, "Why did you even bother to come here if you did not have all the proper paperwork?"

"We did not know that we had to grab all the papers of the bikes or anything else as we left in a panic, wondering if my father was even alive," I tried to explain to him. "I would get all the paperwork and come back another day."

"Why did you even come down here then?" He responded.

I was starting to get pissed off by his attitude, so I reminded him that he was the one who told me to come and pick up my ATV.

"Oh yeah," he said rudely. Then, he took me outside, where the ATV was parked on the side of the station. The Sherriff began to open up the gate to give me the bike. At that moment, stupid me didn't realize that the ATV would not fit in Dad's truck as he had a camper shell on his truck bed. This pissed off Sheriff Sorbal even more than he already was. He told me that he should have had it towed to the impound yard instead of the station.

"Let me go back to the land and get my trailer, so I can take the bike home with me," I said to the sheriff.

"No, you can pick it up from the impound yard in the morning," he responded.

I begged him to let me go back to the land and get the trailer, assuring him that it would only take me around half an hour to do so, but all in vain.

"NO!" He replied obscenely.

So, I called my wife and told her what was going on back at the station with officer Sorbal. She asked me to calm down and to meet her and Grandpa back at the land as they were already headed back. So, I bid officer Sorbal farewell and headed back to the land.

I waited there for about 15 minutes when I noticed a car driving up the dirt road; it was them. They got out of the car, and I noticed that Dad was despondent about Mingo. They told me that Mingo was very badly hurt, with stitches in his head and a fractured skull, so they kept him admitted to the hospital.

All three of us went inside Dad's trailer, where my wife prepared some coffee and cooked us all something to eat. After a nice rest from all of the crap that went down, I reminded Isabell that we had to go back to the station and pick up the ATV. We hooked up the Dirt Bike trailer to the back of Isabell's GMC Yukon and headed back to see officer Sorbal.

As we were pulling up to the station, I noticed that the bike was no longer on the side where it was before. We went inside the station, and Sheriff Sorbal was not there. Only officer Gonzales was there doing his report on everything that happened back at the land. He told us that Sheriff Sorbal had the bike towed to a local impound yard and that we could pick it up from there when they opened. I told Sheriff Gonzales all that went down with Sheriff Sorbal about the bike, but all he said was, "There is nothing I can do as Sheriff Sorbal is my boss."

We hung out there awhile with Sheriff Gonzales to kill time as it was still too early to pick up the bike. We came to find out that he was born and raised in East LA and that he was working up there, waiting to be transferred down to LA, where he hopes to work one day. Sheriff Gonzales was very understanding about everything and was very eager to help us out with everything that happened.

"It seems Sheriff Sorbal has it out for me," I said to him, but he assured me that he was a good cop and meant well.

"There have been all kinds of break-ins all along the desert at various vacation properties. Storage containers were broken into, taking a lot of ATVs and Dune Buggies. Someone even stole a motor home from one guy's property," Sheriff Gonzales told us. "It is the local riff-raff that are doing it. We think one of them may be Sheriff Sorbal's nephew. Maybe that is why he seems pissed off all the time."

When all was said and done, he gave us his card and told us not to worry and that he would be in touch soon. He then said, "As these guys are so stupid that they actually ride the bikes as if they own them, we bust them all the time, but it's mostly only a joyriding charge, so they get out right away. But if we tied these guys to your dad's and Mingo's assault, they would get some serious time."

At last, Isabell and I headed over to the tow yard to pick up the ATV, which ended up costing us a fortune as we had to pay for two tows that night. One where it was found in the desert and towed to the station. The other was when Sheriff Sorbal had it picked up at the station. We paid the tow yard a total of $400, $200 per tow. Then, we loaded up the bike and made our way back to the land to make sure that Dad was okay. As we were driving up the dirt road, we noticed he had already fixed the front gate and was cleaning up the carnage left behind by the assholes that robbed them.

"Everything is okay!" He called out, assuring us. "Go ahead and get back home!"

So, now we headed back to good old San Fernando valley. As we were going back, we started to talk about all that had happened to us out there and wondered if we should tell the boys back home. We finally got home and found that the older boys were both at work, and the little guy Rudy was gone to school. We got the ATV and the trailer put away in the garage and just fell on the couches for some badly needed rest and relaxation. We both ended up falling asleep in the living room.

When the little guy arrived home from school, he woke us up. He started to ask us what had happened at the land and if his Grandpa and Mingo were both okay. We told him that the land was broken into and that his grandpa and Mingo were both attacked and robbed. "All the bikes and riding gear were stolen except that one of the bikes was found in the desert where someone had dumped it," I explained to him. "But don't tell your brothers just yet, as we are not sure how they would react. We will tell them when we'll feel it's the right time."

So, the next thing I did was call the sheriff's station with all the VIN numbers just in case any of the bikes were found.

The following morning the entire family was awake, getting ready for work and school. I was not there as I left for work really early in the morning. Isabell always got up early with me to make my lunch and breakfast for the boys if they were hungry.

As they were all in the kitchen, my wife overheard the two little shits talking about what had happened at the land. It turned out that Rudy could not keep his trap shut and told them all that my wife and I had told him. The two older boys started to give their mom a little crap because we did not tell them what had happened. She told them that we were going to tell them and were just trying to figure out how. So, she started to tell them about what had happened and how the Sheriffs were working on finding out who had done it.

They began to talk to each other, saying how they thought it may have been the guys that rode up on them when they were out riding at jumps the other day. "Maybe those two dudes from the gas station that day were the same guys," one of them claimed.

"Someone should go up there and fuck them up gangster style," the other said. Mom overheard them saying this and got furious.

"Shut the heck up!" She yelled at them. "Especially in front of your little brother." Then she reminded them that the Sheriffs were working on taking care of it.

After the boys left for work and school, Isabell called me up and told me that the boys knew all about what happened and that I should have a nice long talk with them. "I fear that they might try to go up there and do their own kind of Police work," she remarked worriedly.

Later that night at dinner, my wife and I explained to the boys that going up there and trying to get all crazy with people would not help the situation at all and may just end up making matters worse. Their mom and I had got an idea to make flyers from some of the pictures that we had of the bikes and offer a reward to anyone that may have information about their whereabouts. We also decided to mention on the flyers that if anyone had information should contact the sheriff's department. Isabell found some really good pictures of the bikes that she had taken on the weekend when we were out there.

We put down on the flyers that we would pay a $1000 reward for any information that would help us find our bikes. We thought that if the cops caught the bike thieves, they would correspondingly get the guys who robbed the land. So, my wife and I made plans to place the flyers the following weekend at the local liquor stores, gas stations, the little supermarket, and maybe the town Café.

Saturday came real quick. Isabell, the little guy, and I headed up the hill to place flyers and visit Dad and Mingo. As we were headed up Cajon Pass, about 45 minutes out from the land, my cell phone started ringing. And what a coincidence it was; it was Sheriff Gonzales telling me that they found one of the bikes.

"How awesome! Did you make an arrest?" I asked him impatiently.

"Yes. I am at the scene right now. If you can get here ASAP, you can take the bike and avoid any impound charges like the last time," he replied.

"I am around 45 minutes out," I replied. "It just so happened that I am on my way up there."

"Can you get here any sooner?" He asked. "Actually, Sheriff Sorbal is on his way to the scene, and he would make me call the tow yard."

"Where is the bike?" I asked him.

"We are like 10 minutes down HWY 247 from the land," he guided me.

"I am going to send my father down to pick up the bike," I told him. "I will meet you there."

Sheriff Gonzales gave me the address. I immediately called Dad and told him what was going on. He and Mingo flew down, thinking they got the guys that robbed and beat them up. As we pulled up at the scene, we noticed that the bike they found was Dad's old ATC 3-wheeler, and Dad was at the back of the Police car, yelling at the kid they caught with the bike. I saw Sheriff Gonzales trying to calm Dad down.

I ran up to the scene and heard Dad yelling at the young boy in the back of the Police car, telling him he was going to prison for robbery and assault for what they did at his land. The kid was crying and saying that he did not do it and that he knew who did. Right at that moment, Sheriff Sorbal arrived at the scene and told Sheriff Gonzales to get Dad back from the Police car.

I shouted, "The kid knows something about the case! We need to find out exactly what he knows." But my claims went all in vain. Sheriff Sorbal yelled at us to get back and told us that the kid would be questioned at the station later.

While Dad was cussing in Spanish, I was yelling at Sheriff Sorbal, and Isabell was screaming at all of us. In the meantime, the whole neighborhood had got a good size crowd out watching the entire scenario. Sheriff Gonzales got us all to calm down, telling me to get the bike and that he would talk to us later.

The little guy and I started to load the three-wheeler onto my truck when he pointed out that one of the neighbors that had been watching the entire time was one of the guys who was arguing with the boys at the gas station. Right then, I realized just how small that town was really. We finally got Dad and Mingo back into the truck and headed back up to the land.

When we got there, we unloaded the ATC, and Dad put it away back into the storage container. It finally dawned on us that Mingo was back up and around. We then told Dad how we were headed up there to put flyers at all the local shops and stores to help us out in finding the bikes and the guys who hurt and robbed him and Mingo. He did not think that it was a good idea and that it just might get some poor innocent person hurt. Isabell and I started to think about it and decided not to put the flyers.

As we were headed home, we stopped by the sheriff's station to see how things were going with the arrest. Sheriff Gonzales was not there, so the only choice we had was to talk with Sheriff Sorbal. We asked what was going on and what kind of information they were getting from the kid regarding the case.

"The kid did not know anything. He told us that he bought the bike out of the back of a truck in a supermarket parking lot," he told us.

"Is the kid going to jail?" We asked him.

"The charge is possession of a stolen vehicle, which is a misdemeanor, and probably the kid won't even serve any jail time," Sheriff Sorbal told us as my wife, and I just looked at one another in disbelief.

We finally got back to the good old San Fernando Valley and let the boys know what had happened. When we told the boys about the kid that got caught with the bike and that the officer mentioned that he would not get charged with the assault and robbery at the land and would probably be released, they began to make comments that if it had been one of them, they would be looking at ten years in prison. As sad as that sounded, there was a bit of truth to that. Then, the boys told their mom and me that they had plans that evening and were going out. So, Isabell, I, and the little guy decided to get some fast food and called a movie night.

We later come to find out that when those two little shits had actually come up with a stupid plan to get one of their friends, Ray, from down the street, who just so happened to be a lunatic, and go up to Lucerne Valley and try a little detective work of their own. As they began looking all around town for, who knows what, our elder son Junior decided to check out the gas station where they had the confrontation with the two boys from Lucerne Valley, and sure enough, one of the boys was hanging out in front of the store, not the tattooed boy but the other one, Albert Anderson, the one they called Birdman whose girlfriend was the cashier at the store.

The boys pulled up and jumped out of the car, all crazy, and started accusing him of being one of the guys who robbed and beat up their grandpa and Mingo back at the land. As the boy tried to deny it, Ray, being a psycho ass, punched him in the side of his head, knocking him to the floor. Our two sons joined in and started to kick and punch him. As our older son, Junior, and Ray continued to hit the boy on the ground, our middle son, Robert, pulled them off and told them that he had had enough, but Ray didn't listen.

So, our older son grabbed him and made him stop. As my son was arguing with Ray, the boy's girlfriend opened up the store's door and yelled that she had called the cops and that they were on their way. Our sons ran back to the car, but Ray stopped and told the boy that next time, they would kill his ass.

Before the boys even got home that night, my cell phone started ringing. It was Sheriff Gonzales who told me that someone had gone up there and beat up a boy at one of the local liquor stores. He told me that witnesses had claimed that it was three Mexican boys in a dark-colored car. I told him that I did not know anything and assured him that I had just seen my boys and they could not have gone all the way up in Lucerne Valley. I asked if the boy was okay, and he alleged that he had some bumps and bruises but refused to go to the hospital.

I told Sheriff Gonzales that I would talk to both of my boys as soon as they got home and make sure that they did not have anything to do with what had happened to that boy.

"Make sure you really talk to the boys, as I do not want anything to escalate from all that is already going on," he lowkey warned me.

My wife and I feared the worst and waited for them to get home to ask them if they had gone up there and done anything to that boy. Finally, they both came at around 1:30 A.M. Their mom and I started digging into the details to find out if it was them. We told them that Sheriff Gonzales had called and told us that a boy had been beaten up outside a gas station and that someone had seen three Latino boys. They both denied everything and told us that they were down the street at Ray's house, having a few beers. Immediately, they pulled out the racism card.

"We are being blamed because of the way we look!" They claimed.

"The Sheriff was not accusing you guys," I tried to explain to them. "He just called us because he wanted to make sure it wasn't you, as he did not want things to get worse than they already are." They both still denied having anything to do with what happened.

Meanwhile, back up the hill in Lucerne Valley, the boy went home and met with his buddy, tattoo boy Brad Harris, aka Ryder. It turned out that they were the crew that was robbing and stealing from all the different properties. This included Brad Harris (Ryder), his buddy Albert Anderson (Birdman), Sheriff Sorbal's nephew, Scot Hill (Scotty), and Thomas Crooks (Crook.) They were the boys on the dirt bikes that day at the jumps and were also the ones who robbed and beat up Dad and Mingo.

So, the boy told Ryder what had happened back at the gas station and that the three boys knew all about what they had been doing out there before they commenced beating him up.

"I think someone has been talking to the cops," he told Ryder.

Ryder was present at the scene when the ATC was found. He already had suspicions that his buddy who was caught with the three-wheeler, Scott Hill, Sheriff Sobal's nephew, had been talking to the Police. In fear of getting caught, the two boys decided to find out exactly what Scotty told the cops on the day he got arrested with the ATC. Scotty already knew that he was in trouble with the two boys as he wasn't even supposed to be riding the ATC that day. Even though he did not tell the sheriffs anything that day, he knew that the two boys would not believe him, due to which he was already hiding from them.

The next day in the late afternoon, Ryder and Birdman rode over to the boy's house on their Dirt Bikes and told him to get out his bike as they wanted to case out their next job. Nonetheless, their motive was not so. It was to get him all alone and pressure him about telling them what he had told the cops when he got arrested.

"It is kind of late in the day. Maybe you guys should hold off any new jobs as it is hot right now with all that is going on," Scotty told the boys.

They pressured him more, so he decided to go along with them and got all his riding gear and bike out. The three of them headed out into the desert. As the sun went down, Scotty started to wonder what was really going on since he was more and more afraid of the two boys. They stopped the bikes just out past the jumps, somewhat close to the land where Dad and Mingo were outside relaxing after a hard day of work at the Ponderosa.

They got off their bikes and started to ask the kid all kinds of questions about what he told the cops. They told him how three Cholos came up there and jumped Birdman at the gas station and that they knew all kinds of stuff about the robbery up at the land. He tried to tell both of the boys that he did not tell the cops anything.

"All I told them was that I had bought the ATC from someone on the streets," Scotty tried to convince Ryder and Birdman.

They did not believe him and began to rough him up a bit. Then out of nowhere, Ryder pulled out a small handgun to really scare the kid. As Birdman saw the gun, he started to tell Ryder to put the gun away, which led to the both of them arguing with each other about the handgun. Right at that moment, Scotty made a grab for the gun, and it went off, shooting him through his helmet and into his head. Ryder threw the gun back into the Desert, and the two of them tore out on their Dirt Bikes.

Back at the land, Dad and Mingo heard the gunshot and wondered what the heck was going on out there. Dad then suggested to Mingo that they should drive out and make sure that no one was hurt. So, they got in Dad's truck and decided to go and check it out. As they were driving up the dirt road, they noticed that someone was lying in the middle of the road with his motorcycle lying next to him. They got out of the truck and saw that the boy had blood running down his neck. Dad immediately grabbed his phone and called 911 while Mingo took the boy's helmet off.

The boy was still conscious and recognized Mingo and Dad from when they robbed and beat them up. He started to tell them that he was so sorry for what they did to them, but Dad and Mingo were so shaken up about what was going on that they didn't even pay attention to what the boy was telling them. They got the boy in the truck, loaded up his bike, and headed back to the land. As they were heading back, Mingo got a rag holding it on the boy's head, but the kid passed out from the bullet wound. They arrived back at the land, where they waited for the paramedics to arrive.

Soon, both Sheriff Sorbal and Gonzales pulled up with the paramedics and ambulance not too far behind. Sheriff Sorbal saw that it was his nephew and got him loaded up in the ambulance as fast as he could. They rushed him to the closest hospital. Sheriff Sorbal drove off chasing behind the ambulance as he was very worried about his nephew. Sheriff Gonzales stood behind to get statements from Dad and Mingo. After Dad and Mingo gave their statements to Sheriff Gonzales, he told them that he would be back first thing in the morning, as it was now dark out, so that they could take him out to where they found the boy. Dad called us up and started to tell us what had happened with the young boy, not even realizing that it was the kid that was caught with the ATC. We couldn't believe the story that he told us and we were totally stunned. It was like something out of an action movie. We told him that we were planning to come up and see them the following weekend. We said our goodbyes, and then, both Dad and Mingo hit the hay as they were dead tired.

The next day, Sheriff Sorbal and Gonzales showed up at the land right at the crack of dawn as the rooster's cock-a-doodle-do. Dad and Mingo were both already up as they were super early birds. Dad got the little mule out, and he and Mingo headed out to where they found the boy with both sheriffs following close behind in their off-road squad cars. They arrived at the scene, and the blood could still be seen where the boy was lying when they found him. They again explained everything to the sheriffs about how they heard the gunshot, drove out in the truck, saw the boy and took him back to the land, and then called 911, and that's when they both came out. The sheriffs told Dad and Mingo that they could go ahead and return to the land while they stood back and investigated the crime scene.

As the sheriffs were searching all around the area, Sheriff Gonzales saw what appeared to be a handgun lying in the dirt. They picked up the handgun and completed their investigation in the desert. They then headed back to the station with the handgun that Ryder threw in the desert. They had to make sure that it was the gun used to shoot the boy and check the serial numbers in case it had been reported stolen. The boy that was taken to the hospital was in a coma from his head injuries and now fighting for his life.

My wife, the little one, and I headed up to the land on Saturday morning to visit Dad and Mingo and get the scoop on all that was happening out there. Just as Dad was finishing the story which felt like he was telling a movie story, my cell phone started ringing. It was Sheriff Gonzalez with the next big movie scene.

"Where are you?" He asked me.

"It just so happens that I am in your neck of the woods, visiting my father," I told him. "Dad just finished telling Isabell and me all about the boy that had been shot out here a few nights ago." He then hit me with the worst news he could possibly give.

"Where is your son Robert? Where was he the night before last?" He interrogated me.

"What the heck is going on now?" I responded worriedly.

"A small caliber handgun was found at the scene where the boy was shot, and it just so happens to be registered under Robert's name. We need him to come in for questioning right away," the Sherriff finished saying, hitting me with a major shock.

"What the heck? It doesn't make any sense!" I told him, baffled.

Right then, it blasted in my head, and I remembered that I had stashed my son's gun in the storage container before all this shit went down. So, the next moment, my wife and I got the little guy and hauled our ass to the sheriff's station to plead our case and tell them that I had taken that gun from my son and hid it in Dad's storage container.

As we were driving to the station, I told Isabell all about the gun and how the boys had taken it to the land to shoot and reminded her of the time we heard gunshots. She was pissed off that neither did I tell her that the boys had a gun nor about taking and hiding it. I tried to tell her that I had forgotten about the gun with all the crap that was going on and that I meant to tell her. She was furious, plus with the fact that her son might get the blame for the shooting, she stopped talking to me.

We got to the station, and both Gonzales and Sorbal were there. I went to them and told them my story about the storage container and how, whoever had the gun, was the guy involved in beating and robbing Dad and Mingo. Isabell also told the officers that Robert was at home that Thursday night when the shooting occurred and that there was no way that he could have done this.

"I believe the storage container story as I was already thinking that these guys did this to one of their own because I noticed two sets of Dirt Bike tracks leaving the scene where the boy was shot," Sheriff Gonzales said.

I could see that Sheriff Sorbal was having a hard time believing our story, but it was the truth. I told Isabell not to worry and that everything would be okay. Sheriff Gonzales then told us that the boy who was shot was the same boy who was caught with Dad's ATC.

"Okay, so my son goes back out there to kill him! Come on! No way is he going to go out there and do something like that and really leave his gun at the scene of the crime!" I said to them rudely. "He is being set up!"

We also told them that my wife and I both saw our son at home that night and that there was no way that he could have driven all the way out to Lucerne Valley since we both saw him in the house around the time the shooting occurred.

"I was the one who had taken the gun from my son, so there was no way that he could have done this. It is all my fault that this is happening. I forgot all about the gun that I took from him," I regretted. "Only if I had remembered, we would have reported the gun stolen along with everything else, and my boy would be in the clear."

We got back home with the worst news that we could possibly have and told our son Robert all about the shooting in the desert, his gun that was found at the scene, and that they wanted him to turn himself in for questioning. He could not believe his ears. I told him that it was my fault and that we were going to do everything to make things right. We also told him not to worry since we all saw him at home that night and that we would hire a lawyer to make sure that he did not get the blame for shooting that boy.

“Dad, you know they are going to arrest me for that shooting,” he said to me. Sure enough, he was right. We got him to go with us to the sheriff’s station, thinking that they just wanted to talk to him and that for sure he would be able to come back home. But oh boy, how wrong we were! Right when we got to the station, Sheriff Sorbal came up to us, read Robert his rights, handcuffed him, and took him to the back.

He told Isabell and me that our son was being held for attempted murder and assault with a deadly weapon. My wife just about fainted when he said that to us, and my heart just dropped to the floor. As much as we tried to explain our son’s innocence to both Sheriff Sorbal and Gonzales, they said that there was nothing that they could do for us as the gun was registered under our son’s name and there was a reason for him to go up there and commit that crime.

Around three weeks went by, and our son was now transferred to the San Bernardino County Jail, awaiting a court date for his arraignment. We hired one of the best lawyers we could afford, who told us if all was true, he would be able to get off. Isabell took time off from work as she had been going to see Robert at least twice a week and was still very mad at me. I had been staying in contact with Sheriff Gonzales to see if there were any more break-ins up there. He told me no and that they had not received any calls lately.

Down, In The Valley

I guessed that the boys were lying low for a while. I had been keeping in touch with Dad but did not go to see him as we were just too busy with all that was going on with our son. He kept calling and asking us if he was home yet and to keep on praying and keeping our heads up.

Two months went by, and now, our boy's court date was scheduled for the coming Monday. Our lawyer said that it was only for him to make his plea, and they would set another court day for the trial to start. My wife and I became depressed since all the court crap had been going on to the point that we hardly even spoke to each other. The little guy went to school every day, and our older boy, Junior, would just go to work. They would come home and not say much. Anyone could see the sadness in all of us because of all that happened.

We were waiting for the weekend since we were all set for court on Monday. Isabell and I were very nervous about everything. Out of nowhere, my cell phone rang; it was from Sheriff Gonzales. I showed the phone to my wife, and we both wondered what he wanted with us now. So without knowing it, I answered the call to get the best news we had in a long time.

“I have the greatest news you could ever imagine,” he started to say.

“What is it?” I asked petulantly.

“The boy in the coma, Scotty, has recovered and come up. He says he is going to testify on Ryder and Birdman for shooting him, and he made a plea deal for the robbery and assault on Mingo and your dad," he told me delightedly. "Most of all, your son is innocent of shooting him."

I could not believe my ears. He went on to say that the kid felt so bad when he found out that it was Dad and Mingo who saved his life that he just felt that telling the truth was the right thing to do.

It has been a couple of months now, and the boys are all doing great. Isabell and I are back on normal speaking terms, and we are all planning a big Labor Day camping trip back at the Ponderosa with Dad and Mingo. We all have learned some valuable lessons from all that happened. More so, the incident has brought us all just a little bit closer. But every now and then, they all - Isabell, Dad, Mingo, and all the three boys – Jokingly throw the handgun thing back in my face.

Oh well! I guess that's what life is like in the big valley.

The End

Arthur De Anda

Thank You

Made in the USA
Las Vegas, NV
02 April 2023

70075325R00036